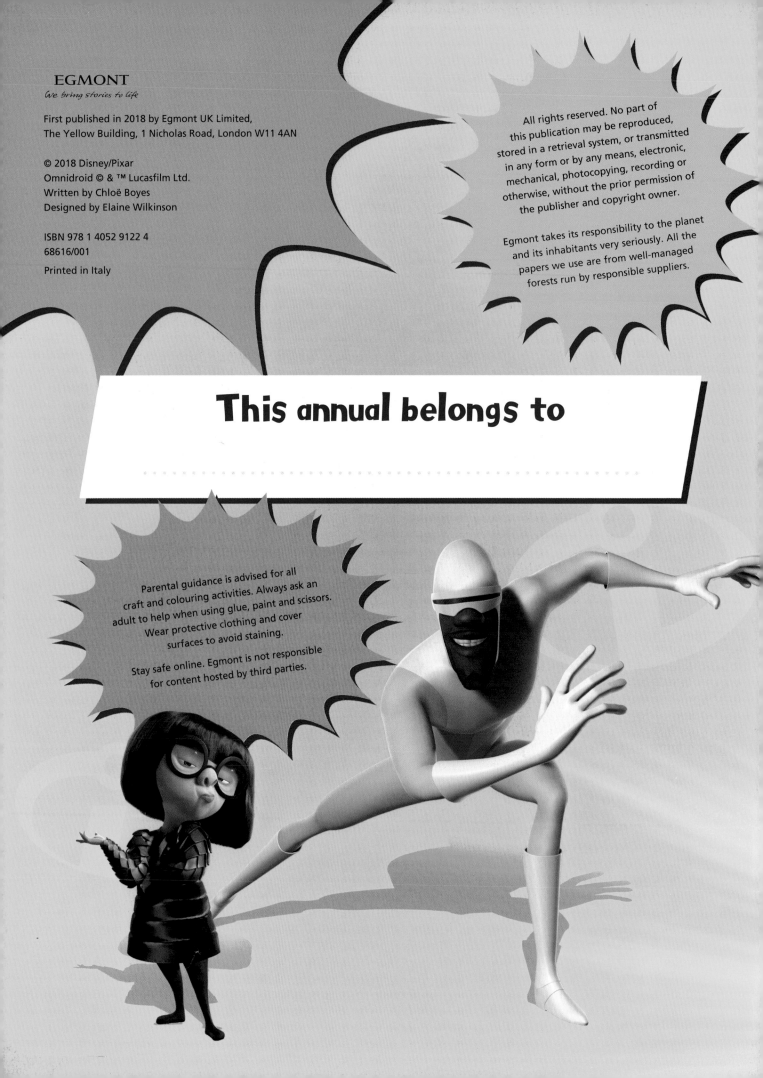

EGMONT
We bring stories to life

First published in 2018 by Egmont UK Limited,
The Yellow Building, 1 Nicholas Road, London W11 4AN

© 2018 Disney/Pixar
Omnidroid © & ™ Lucasfilm Ltd.
Written by Chloë Boyes
Designed by Elaine Wilkinson

ISBN 978 1 4052 9122 4
68616/001

Printed in Italy

This annual belongs to

Parental guidance is advised for all craft and colouring activities. Always ask an adult to help when using glue, paint and scissors. Wear protective clothing and cover surfaces to avoid staining.

Stay safe online. Egmont is not responsible for content hosted by third parties.

Disney · PIXAR

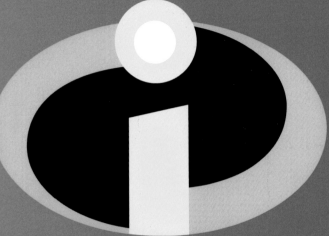

The Incredibles

ANNUAL 2019

CONTENTS

THE INCREDIBLES MOVIE

1

Mr Incredible is a Super from Municiberg, with the power of extreme strength. He is married to another Super, Elastigirl. Elastigirl has the power of flexibility and shape-shifting.

2

Mr Incredible's biggest fan is a boy called Buddy. Buddy dreams of being a Super and has invented lots of gadgets to give him his own powers. He begs Mr Incredible to let him be his sidekick, "Incrediboy", and follows him in secret when Mr Incredible says no. Eventually, Mr Incredible gets cross with Buddy and tells him that he works alone.

3

One day, Mr Incredible saves someone who doesn't want to be saved and they make a complaint against him. One by one, more people make complaints against Supers and it is decided they must go into hiding and live normal lives.

4

15 years later, Mr Incredible and Elastigirl are living as Bob and Helen Parr with their three children Violet, Dash and Jack-Jack. They all try very hard to be normal, but with their powers it's tough.

5

Bob misses the Super days and persuades his best friend Lucius (who used to be Super, Frozone) to listen in to Police radios and try to stop crime. He hates his job working for an insurance company and especially hates his boss, Mr Huph.

6

Mr Incredible receives a secret message from a woman named Mirage. She tells him that Supers are still working and they would like him to help them. Bob travels to Nomanisan Island to help defeat the Omnidroid, a robot which they've lost control of.

7

Mr Incredible destroys the robot and is asked back to the island again. But this time, Bob realises that Mirage works for Buddy, Mr Incredible's old follower. Buddy was so angry when Mr Incredible rejected him that he became Syndrome, a Super who planned to defeat Mr Incredible and become famous for saving Municiberg.

8

Helen realises that something is not right. She finds Bob's old Mr Incredible suit has been repaired and visits their friend and fashion designer, Edna Mode, to see what's going on. Helen finds out that Edna has made a new Mr Incredible suit and has also made suits for the whole Parr family.

9

Edna tells Helen that each suit contains a tracking device. Helen tracks Bob's location and finds out he's been lying about work. She is worried he's in trouble and decides to go after him. What Helen doesn't realise, is that Violet and Dash have hidden away on her plane and are travelling with her to Nomanisan Island, leaving their baby brother with a babysitter.

10

Back on the island, Mr Incredible has been captured by Syndrome's men and has been locked away.

11

Helen leaves the kids hiding inside a cave whilst she searches for Bob. But suddenly, the cave fills with fire and Violet and Dash only just get away. They find their Mum and Dad but before they can escape the island, Syndrome captures them all.

12

They discover Syndrome's plan to release the Omnidroid in Municiberg and then show how Super he can be by saving everybody. Once Syndrome leaves to carry out his plan, the Parrs convince Mirage to help them escape. They race back to Municiberg to save the day.

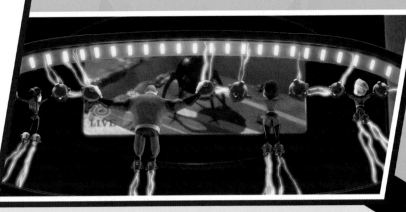

13

Back in Municiberg, the family work together to defeat the Omnidroid, with a bit of help from their friend Frozone.

14

After defeating the Omnidroid, the family arrive home, but Jack-Jack is no longer with the babysitter. Syndrome has kidnapped Jack-Jack and flies into the air with him. Helen tries to save him but, before she can, the baby transforms into a monster, making Syndrome drop him. As he falls, Jack-Jack breaks Syndrome's rocket boots and Syndrome falls to earth. Helen shape-shifts into a parachute and carries Jack-Jack to safety.

15

Three months later, the Parrs are watching Dash race, when a new super villain, the Underminer, appears. The Parrs put on their Super masks, ready for battle.

THE END

A.K.A. MR INCREDIBLE

Mr Incredible is a tough and brave Super, husband of Elastigirl and Dad to Violet, Dash and Jack-Jack.

"Saving the day, one day at a time."

Powers

Extreme **strength**. Mr Incredible can lift very heavy objects.

He can jump very high in the air and has very strong senses so he can spot danger more easily.

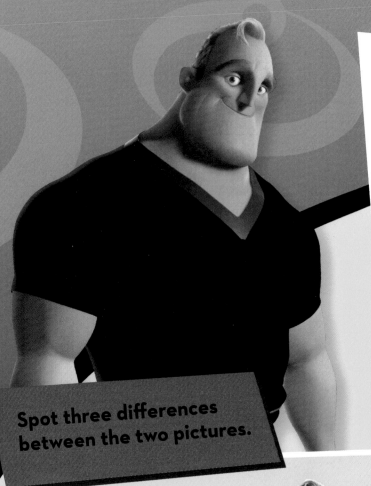

In **The Incredibles** movie: Mr Incredible is the ultimate Super and loves helping to stop the bad guys. He does not cope well when Supers are sent into hiding and still tries to fight crime in secret.

When an undercover mission leads to his capture, Mr Incredible needs the help of his family to escape Syndrome and save Municiberg.

Spot three differences between the two pictures.

Meet Helen Parr

A.K.A. ELASTIGIRL

Elastigirl is smart, strong-willed and fiercely independent.

"Girls, c'mon! Leave the saving of the world to the men? I don't think so!"

Powers

Elastigirl's main Super power is **elasticity**. She can stretch huge distances and bend or twist into any shape.

She can jump up to 25 metres and stretch over 91 metres!

In **The Incredibles** movie: Elastigirl cares about protecting people and stopping bad guys. After Supers are outlawed in Municiberg and sent into hiding, Helen proves to be as super at running her family as she had been at catching criminals.

Wife to Mr Incredible and Mum to Super kids Violet, Dash and Jack-Jack, Helen is great at keeping everyone in check.

When Mr Incredible gets into trouble during a secret mission, Helen rescues him and puts the Parr family back together, so they can defeat super villain, Syndrome, as a team.

Find the missing pieces of the jigsaw to finish this picture of Elastigirl!

Colour the logo next to the correct pieces

a

d

c

b

Meet The Parr Kids

VIOLET, DASH AND JACK-JACK

Violet, Dash and Jack-Jack are the children of Elastigirl and Mr Incredible.

Violet and Dash know they have Super powers but must live day-to-day as normal kids, which can be hard sometimes.

VIOLET

"Normal? What does anyone in this family know about being normal?"

Powers
Can produce **force fields** to protect herself and those around her.

OMNIDROID ATTACK

a

Syndrome is training the Omnidroids to defeat Mr Incredible. He has changed each machine very slightly, apart from two.

b

c

Find the matching pair.

d

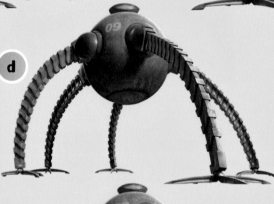

e

Frozone helps to defeat the Omnidroid by freezing its legs!

Check your answer on page 68.

CALL EDNA!

Start

Check your answer on page 68.

Mr Incredible is planning another secret mission, but his Supersuit is damaged.

Finish

Help him find the way to Edna Mode's house so he can get it repaired.

DRAW
JACK-JACK

Follow the steps to draw Jack-Jack.

1 First, draw an oval shape for the head with 2 small circles for ears.

2 Next, add a spike of hair to the top of the head and add lines for Jack-Jack's nose and mouth.

3 Add a figure of 8 shape for the mask.

4

Now draw 2 circles inside your 8 shape for Jack-Jack's eyes.

5

Colour in your drawing and Jack-Jack will be ready!

FORCE FIELDS

Count how many force fields this Super has made.

There are [ ] force fields.

Check your answer on page 68.

Trace over the letters to spell her name.

Violet

22

DASH'S BIG RACE

Dash is desperate to compete in the running race.

Start

Help him to the finish by tracking which way he is facing to make a path.

Finish

Check your answer on page 68.

23

ELASTIGIRL'S CODE CRACKER

Elastigirl must unscramble the code to work out where Mr Incredible is and who has captured him.

First, colour in her Supersuit and then follow the letters in the wheel to get the clues.

24

Write your answers in the spaces below.

Start

L A N D S Y N D R O M E

S _ _ _ _ _ _ _ _ _

N _ _ _ _ _ _ _ _

I _ _ _ _ _ _ _ _

Check your answers on page 68.

25

ICE PUZZLE

Start

Frozone can create ice bridges or slopes to skate across.

Check your answer on page 68.

Trace the ice path Frozone has made and count the number of shields you pass.

There are ☐ shields.

26

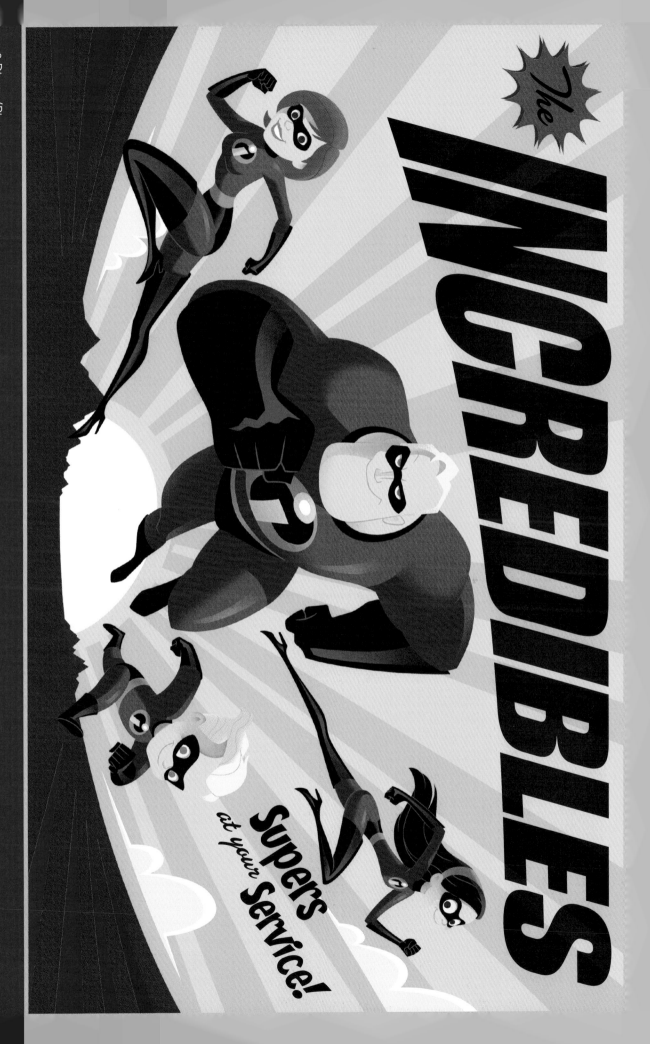

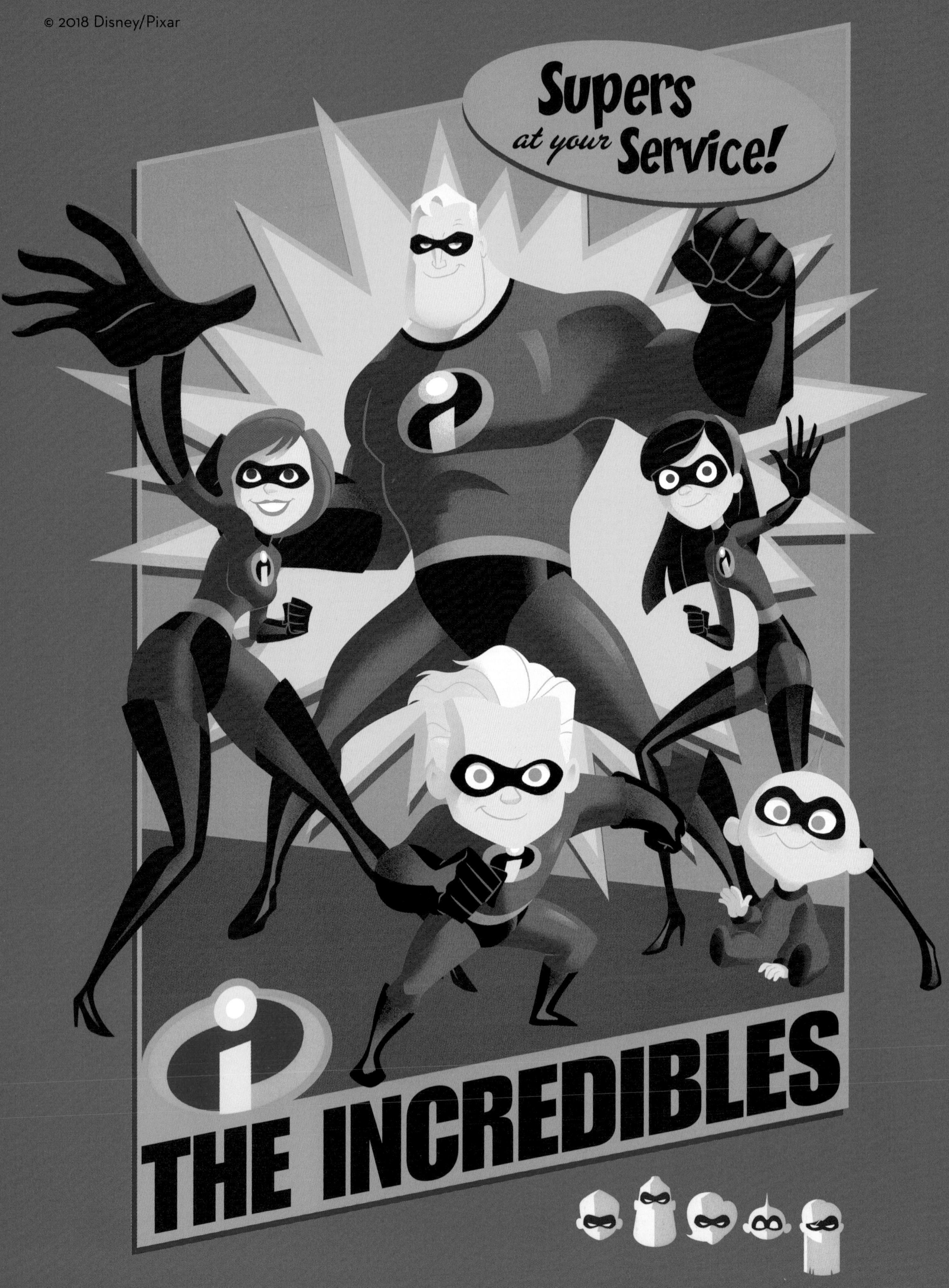
Supers at your Service!
THE INCREDIBLES

SYNDROME'S PLAN

Syndrome is out to get Mr Incredible. Spot 6 differences between the pictures.

Colour in a tick each time you find a difference.

Check your answers on page 68.

HOW INCREDIBLE

If you live near the Incredibles, you're bound to see some amazing things. Can you answer these Incredible questions?

1 Can you point to 3 pink things in the main picture?

2 How many flowers can you see in the picture?

2²
1 3

3 What do the numbers on the tyre add up to?

Check your answers on page 68.

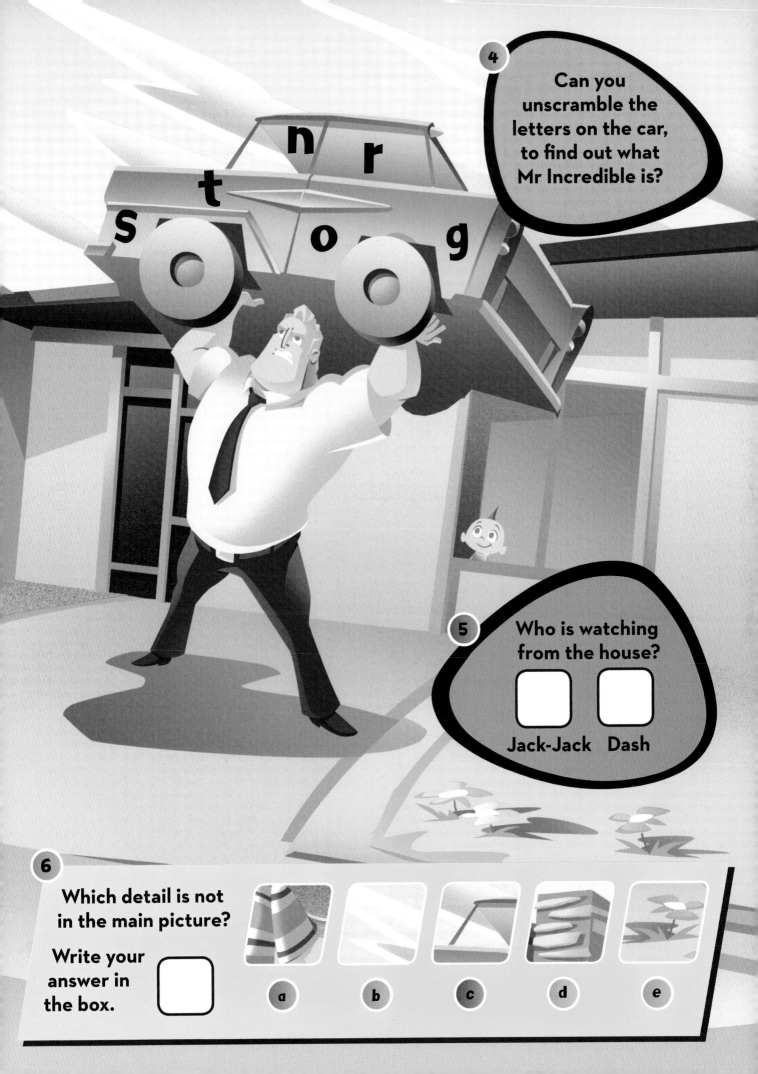

DOUBLE TROUBLE!

Use your brightest pens to colour this picture of Dash looking at his reflection.

SYNDROME

Powers

None. Syndrome invents gadgets to give him Super powers, including rocket boots which make him fly.

"EVERYONE can be super! And when everyone's super ... no one will be!"

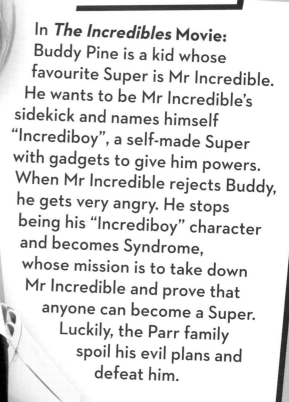

In ***The Incredibles* Movie:** Buddy Pine is a kid whose favourite Super is Mr Incredible. He wants to be Mr Incredible's sidekick and names himself "Incrediboy", a self-made Super with gadgets to give him powers. When Mr Incredible rejects Buddy, he gets very angry. He stops being his "Incrediboy" character and becomes Syndrome, whose mission is to take down Mr Incredible and prove that anyone can become a Super. Luckily, the Parr family spoil his evil plans and defeat him.

FLYING
FRIENDS

You will need
- glue · card
- · scissors
- · a hole punch · string
- · a drinking straw

Photocopy the page if you don't want to cut it out.

Ask a grown-up for help when using scissors

1. Glue the characters and the scene on to card and then cut them out.

2. Tie some lengths of string to a drinking straw. Stick each of the characters to a piece of string.

3. Ask an adult to help you punch a hole at the top of each character.

4. Now make the characters fly over the scene!

Fold here

Fold here

THE UNDERMINER

The Underminer is a mole-like man.

Powers
Burrowing underground. Using a gigantic tunneller he can travel under the city, breaking into bank vaults and causing mayhem.

"Behold, the Underminer! I'm always beneath you, but nothing is beneath me!"

In **The Incredibles** Movie: The Underminer appears at the very end of the movie, when the Parr family come together to defeat him. *Incredibles 2* begins with the Parrs fighting the Underminer as he tries to destroy Municiberg.

ESCAPE PLAN

The Incredibles must find their way back to Municiberg to stop Syndrome.

a   b   c

Check your answer on page 68.

Unscramble the paths to work out which route takes them home.

TV TROUBLE

1

One night, the Parr family decided to watch TV. "I want to watch cartoons," said Dash. "But I want to watch a film!" cried Violet. So, they began to argue.

2

Then, the TV suddenly started to whizz through different channels. The Parrs all stopped arguing and stared at the fuzzy screen.

3

"What's happening?" asked Dash. "Either someone has the remote control, or there is something very strange going on," laughed Bob. "I don't have it," said Dash.

4

So, the Parrs decided to use their Super powers to search for the remote. Bob lifted up the sofa and looked underneath but the remote wasn't there.

5

"I wonder if it's up here?" puzzled Helen, as she stretched up to search on the shelves. But there was no sign of the remote there, either.

6

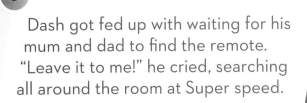

Dash got fed up with waiting for his mum and dad to find the remote. "Leave it to me!" he cried, searching all around the room at Super speed.

7

As they all searched, the room got messier and messier. "Stop!" shouted Violet, as she used her force field to save her from falling objects.

8

Everyone stopped and looked around the room. "Look at the mess you've made," Violet pointed out. And they still hadn't found the remote!

9 Suddenly, they noticed Jack-Jack. He had been hiding underneath the table all along, playing with the remote and changing channels!

10 "Oh, Jack-Jack, look at all the TV trouble you've caused!" laughed Bob. "And now, I guess we should use our Super powers to clean up!" giggled Helen.

THE END

ABOUT THE STORY

1 Who wanted to watch cartoons?

2 What did Bob lift up and look underneath?

3 What saved Violet from falling objects?

4 Who had the remote, all along?

Check your answers on page 68.

SUPER CUFFS

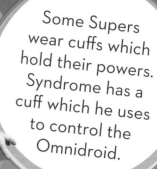

Some Supers wear cuffs which hold their powers. Syndrome has a cuff which he uses to control the Omnidroid.

You will need
- 2 toilet rolls
- scissors · glue
- coloured card
- buttons

Make your own cuffs using the steps below.

Ask a grown-up for help when using scissors

1

Cut along the length of the toilet rolls.

2

Paint your cuffs and decorate them with sequins or glitter or cut out shapes from coloured card to glue on.

3

Use a hole-punch to make holes along the edges that you've cut.

4

Use the string to tie on your cuffs and try them on. You're ready to fight the baddies!

Thread string through the holes like you would thread laces.

SAVING THE DAY
ONE DAY AT A TIME

INCREDIBLES 2

Disney · PIXAR

SUPER VIOLET

Who is Violet protecting with her force field?

p
z
i
n
s
f
o
a
r
d
h
z
o
r
f
n
i
p

Cross out the letters that appear twice to find out the answer!

Jack-Jack

Dash

Elastigirl

Mr Incredible

Check your answer on page 68.

FULL TEAM

This is a game for two players. Choose a player card each and take turns to roll the dice. Move your counter around the board, the number of spaces you roll. Each time you land on a character space, tick them off on your player card. Keep going around until you have collected all of the characters. The first one to get a complete set wins!

PLAYER CARD 1

Start

You will need
- 2 counters
- a dice

PLAYER CARD 2

WE ARE INCREDIBLE

Disney · PIXAR

INCREDIBLES 2

DESIGN YOUR OWN
SUPERSUIT

Every Super needs a Supersuit. Design your own amazing Supersuit below.

Remember to colour your suit in.

47

A HELPING HAND

Mr Incredible is hurrying home. Can you lead him to his family, lending a helping hand five times on the way?

Start

Finish

Check your answer on page 68.

SPOT WITH JACK-JACK

How many of each item below can you count in the picture? Write the correct numbers in the boxes.

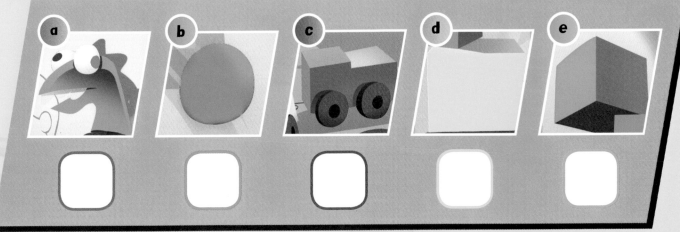

a

b

c

d

e

WHAT'S YOUR SUPER NAME?

Use the name generator to work out your Super name.

Take the first letter of your name:

A Awesome

B Fire

C Sky

D Ice

E Tornado

F Bionic

G Super

H Iron

I Crimson

J Doctor

K Atomic

L Agent

M Giant

N Steel

O Night

P The Flying

Q Psychic

R Magic

S Thunder

T Mighty

U The Amazing

V Wonder

W Lightning

X Howling

Y Ultra

Z Green

January	Frost
February	Shadow
March	Eagle
April	Ray
May	Master
June	Trooper
July	Hero

And the month of your birthday:

August	Blaster
September	Dragon
October	Ranger
November	Storm
December	Spark

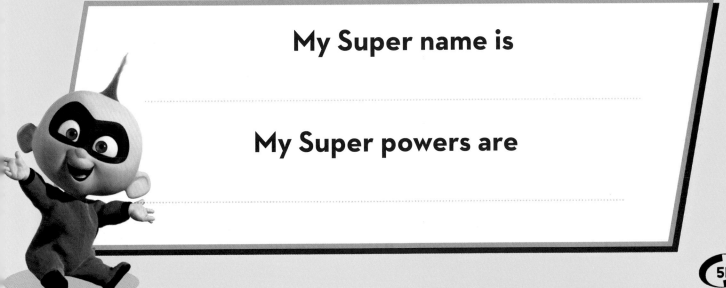

My Super name is

....

My Super powers are

....

51

SUPER MASK

A Super's identity is their most secret weapon. Make your own Super mask to keep your identity a secret.

You will need
• tracing paper
• pencil • coloured card
• scissors • hole-punch
• glue • string

Ask a grown-up for help when using scissors •

1 Trace a template from the next page onto paper and stick onto coloured card.

2 Cut out your mask shape. Ask an adult to cut out the eye holes for you and use a hole punch to make holes for the string.

3 Using a different colour of card, draw and cut out shapes to stick to your mask. Add glitter, sequins and buttons – anything you can find at home to make your mask special.

4 Thread string through the holes and tie in a knot at the front to keep them secure. Ask an adult to fix the mask on for you and tie it up at the back.

Now, you're ready to save the day!

MEMORY CHALLENGE

Take a look at the scene below, then cover it up and see how many of the questions you can answer.

1 What colour is Helen's bag?

2 Is Dash in the scene?

3 How many people are in the picture?

4 Is there a green car in the picture?

Check your answers on page 68.

Disney · PIXAR

Incredibles 2

In *Incredibles 2* the Parrs battle more villains and take on new tasks to try and keep the public safe. But will they convince the world that Supers are a force for good?

ALL SHAPES
AND SIZES

Put the characters in order from smallest to biggest. Write the letters in the boxes below.

smallest ——————————————————➤ largest

Check your answer on page 68.

56

SEQUENCES

Check your answers on page 68.

Which image comes next in each sequence? Draw your answer in the box.

a

b

c

d

57

INCREDIBLES 2
THE MOVIE

PART TWO: When the first movie ended, the Parr family were preparing to defeat the Underminer, a super villain who had drilled through the city in his gigantic drilling machine! The second movie starts from here – read on to discover whether the Parrs save Municiberg ...

1

The Underminer is tunnelling under the city and stealing money from bank vaults. As the Supers close in, the Underminer escapes with the stolen money, but his machine is still raging through the streets and it's headed straight for City Hall.

2

Elastigirl and Mr Incredible manage to stop the tunneller but it has already caused quite a lot of damage to the city.

3

The police are very angry at the Supers for letting the Underminer get away and remind them that Supers are still illegal. The police take the family to the motel they are living in (their home was destroyed by Syndrome at the end of the first movie) and tell them this is the last time they will be helping – the Parrs are on their own now.

4

Just when the family thought Super life was over, their friend Lucius comes to visit. He says he's been contacted by a business tycoon who wants to help Supers and make them legal again.

5

The Parrs visit a man called Winston who owns a technology company called DevTech. Together with his sister, Evelyn, Winston wants to film Elastigirl saving people to show the public how valuable Supers could be.

6

Elastigirl gets a new Supersuit with a built-in camera and a jet-powered, electric Elasticycle from Evelyn. She jumps on her bike and zooms to her first mission. Meanwhile, Bob stays at home and looks after Violet, Dash and Jack-Jack.

7

Elastigirl watches the unveiling of a new hovertrain in the city. But suddenly, the train shoots out of the station the wrong way.

8

Elastigirl races after it and transforms into a parachute, bringing the train to a stop and saving the passengers. Suddenly, a message appears on the engineer's control panel:

"Welcome back, Elastigirl — The Screenslaver."

9

Back at home, Bob has fallen asleep and Jack-Jack escapes from the house and fights a raccoon in the family's garden – now he can travel through doors and burst into flames. Bob wakes up, but it's too late.

10

The baby is shooting laser beams out of his eyes and multiplying so there are lots of Jack-Jacks. How will Bob keep track?

11

Following Elastigirl's successful train rescue, Winston sets up a TV interview for her. But whilst she's on air, a hypnotic pattern appears on screen and the news anchor, in a trance, says, "Screens are everywhere. We are controlled by screens. And screens are controlled by me, the Screenslaver!"

12

Next, the Screenslaver threatens to crash a helicopter with an important ambassador on board. Elastigirl jumps out of the window and saves the ambassador, just in time.

13

Elastigirl is doing a great job and Winston invites Supers from all over the world to come out of hiding together. But Elastigirl is worried that Screenslaver is still at large. She sets up a broadcast to entice the Screenslaver to try and take control and then tracks the signal to find out where the villain is hiding. The signal leads her into an apartment full of hypnotising equipment.

14

As Elastigirl is looking around, the Screenslaver enters the room, wearing a mask. The Screenslaver jumps out of the window but Helen follows and captures him by stretching herself into a parachute.

15

When she unmasks him, the Screenslaver is just a confused man who has no idea how he ended up wearing the Screenslaver costume. Even after the police arrest him, he is sure he is innocent.

16

Back at home, Bob is finding things hard. Jack-Jack has morphed into a monster and is chasing after Violet. Bob goes to see Edna, an old friend. At first, Edna refuses to help but when Jack-Jack starts to use his powers to make himself look like her, she agrees to take care of him.

17

Winston and Evelyn throw a party to celebrate Elastigirl's success. But Elastigirl feels that something isn't right and sneaks off to watch the footage recorded from her Supersuit camera. While she's re-watching the footage, Evelyn comes into the room and forces a pair of hypnotic goggles on Elastigirl, putting her in a trance.

18

Evelyn traps Elastigirl in a sub-zero room, so that if she tries to stretch her way out, she'll break! She tells Elastigirl that she was the Screenslaver all along – she hypnotised a pizza delivery guy to wear the costume so he would take the blame.

19

Bob picks Jack-Jack up from Edna's house. Edna has made Jack-Jack his own Supersuit, fitted with a tracking device. Bob gets a call from Evelyn, telling him Elastigirl's in trouble and he must come immediately to the DevTech yacht.

20

When Bob arrives, a hypnotised Elastigirl forces goggles onto Bob. Now they're both in a trance!

21

Six hypnotised Supers visit the Parr kids and try to take them, but Frozone stops the baddies and the kids manage to escape. They know their parents are in trouble – the yacht has sailed with them on board. Dash changes the Incredible car into a speedboat and they race after them.

Evelyn's plan is to power the boat into the city and make Supers look like villains. She must be stopped!

22

The kids find their parents and smash up the controls on the boat, releasing them from their trance. Elastigirl chases after Evelyn and Mr Incredible tries to stop the boat.

23

As the boat reaches land, Violet casts a force field to protect everyone from harm. The boat comes to a halt and everyone is saved! Evelyn is taken away by the police and the Parr family are back together again!

THE END

MUNICIBERG TIMES

SUPERS LEGAL!

WHICH CHARACTER ARE YOU?

Are you strong, like Mr Incredible or creative, like Edna? Each character has something special.

CHOOSE A VILLAIN

Syndrome

How do you travel?

Bike

Skateboard

Pick an activity

Your perfect weekend activity would be

Listening to music

Reading a magazine alone

Building a treehouse

Bowling with friends

Jack-Jack

Violet

Mr Incredible

Frozone

Answer the questions to find out who you're most like.

TO DEFEAT

The Underminer

Pick a Super skill

Running very fast

Jumping very high

Pick an animal

Lion

Would you prefer to

Cheetah

Paint a picture

Play a team sport

Dash

Edna

Elastigirl

THE INCREDIBLES

QUIZ

It's time to put your *Incredibles* knowledge to the test! See how many of the questions you can answer.

Colour the circle next to your answer.

1 True or false, Dash has the power of Super speed?

 True    False

2 True or false, the Underminer is part man and part horse?

 True    False

3 How many children do Helen and Bob have?

 2    3    4

4 What is the machine that Syndrome uses to attack Municiberg?

 Omnidroid    Atattack 2000

5

What is Frozone's secret identity?

Buddy

Lucius

6

Who does Bob visit to repair his Supersuit?

Edna

Frozone

7

Who flies the plane to Nomanisan Island?

Helen

Violet

Check your answers on page 68.

P13.

P15. b and c

P18. b and d

P19.

P22. there are 7 force fields

P23.

P25. SYNDROME, NOMANISAN ISLAND

P26. Frozone found 10 shields.

P29.

P30-31.

1. Pink items: butterfly, bubblegum, flower.
2. There are **4** flowers.
3. The numbers add up to **8**.
4. STRONG
5. Jack-Jack is watching
6. **e** is not in the picture

P37. b

P40.

1. Dash wanted to watch cartoons.
2. Bob lifted up the sofa.
3. Violet's force fields saved her from falling objects.
4. Jack-Jack had the remote.

P43. Dash

P48.

P49. a 1, b 3, c 1, d 2, e 4.

P54.

1. Helen's bag is blue.
2. Dash is not in the scene.

3. There are three people in the picture.
4. There is a green car.

P56.

From the smallest to the biggest.
e, d, a, c, b

P57.

a

b

c

d

P66-67.

1. True
2. False (he is part man part mole)
3. 3
4. Omnidroid
5. Lucius
6. Edna
7. Helen

THE END